LUDMILA

BOOKS BY PAUL GALLICO

LUDMILA

BY

PAUL GALLICO

Drawings by Reisie Lonette

Doubleday & Company, Inc., Garden City, New York

1959

Library of Congress Catalog Card Number 59-8002
Copyright © 1959 by Doubleday & Company, Inc.
All Rights Reserved
Printed in the United States of America
Designed by Diana Klemin

To Baroness Ludmila Von Falz-Fein

LUDMILA

Part way up the valley from Steg, in the Principality of Liechtenstein, where the torrent Malbun comes tumbling down its glacial bed from the peaks of the *Ochsenkopf* and *Silberhorn,* you will find the shrine of Saint Ludmila, *die heilige Notburga,* in a niche cut into the solid rock above the rushing waters.

It is a sweet figure in milkmaid's dress with the golden rays of the sun behind her head in place of the usual halo. In one hand she holds a harvesting sickle, and in the other a milk jug, for she is the patron saint of the dairymen, the herdsmen, milkers, butter separators and cheese makers, and the taupe-colored Alpine cattle with the broad heads, curving horns, and large, gentle eyes are under her special protection.

Indeed, her connection with such is plain for all to see since beneath the feet of the figure there is affixed the whitened skull and grayish horns of what must once have been rather a small cow.

The younger generations, no longer brought up as were their fathers on the legends of the mountains, are unaware of its significance, but many of the local patriarchs remember what they learned at their mother's knee of the miracle that happened more than a hundred years ago, performed by the holy Notburga, the sainted milkmaid, the time of the annual return of the cattle at the end of the summer from the high pasturage to Vaduz in the Rhine Valley below.

All those connected with the event are long since dead, Alois, the bearded, hardheaded, chief herdsman and his brown-haired daughter, Ludmila, who was then only seven, and named after the saint, Father Polda, the mountain priest, chaplain of Steg, and of course the little Weakling, whose skull and horns adorn the shrine of the patron saint of all milch cows.

However, you may still see the gay and colorful ceremony that takes place in Liechtenstein each autumn when the first threat of snow comes to the high passes and the cattle begin to cough in the early gusts of cold wind that sweep down from the *Sareiserjoch* and the glaciers behind the *Wildberg* and *Panülerkopf.*

There is a valley tucked away behind the granite wall of the

Three Sisters above Schaan, in Liechtenstein, the *Saminatal*, leading to Malbun, five thousand feet above the meandering Rhine. It is famous for its rich grass and quiet, protected pasturage, where are to be encountered from time to time scattered plants of that herb not found in the lowlands, one of the rare *Garbengewächse*, of the Species *Alchemilla*, which the Liechtensteiners call by the beautiful name of *Mutterkraut*— or "Mothers weed," for it is believed to increase the flow of milk, and the herdsmen are invariably on the lookout for the yellow-flowered broad-leafed plants which seem to grow best in those shaded spots where the snow has lain the longest during the winter when the valley is buried under snow and ice.

It is the custom of the peasants in Liechtenstein each spring to send their cattle up into the mountains and through the tunnel cut through a quarter mile of solid rock near Steg that gives access to this hidden, enchanted valley. They go in charge of herdsmen, dairymen, and cheese makers, who move up with the beasts, taking their families with them in horse-drawn wooden carts.

There they remain for the entire summer, living in the high Alpine huts, tending the cattle at pasturage, milking them, making the rich yellow cheeses and creamy butter on the spot and keeping careful record of the yield of each animal. There is no contact with the valley below. Herds and herdsmen vanish, not to reappear until mid-September.

But then, what a day!

The peasants come from miles around to gather at Gnalp, below the Kulm at the mouth of the tunnel. From Triesen,

Vaduz, Balzers, and Schaan, in the *Rheintal* below, the citizens climb the mountain, lining the winding roads, to cheer and wave to the returning wanderers, crowding as close as possible to see which and whose cow will be the first to emerge from the tunnel, leading all the rest as signal of her championship.

The *Abfahrt* or descent takes place in the early morning with the sun shining over the *Rheintal,* warming the first nip in the clear mountain air. At first there is only the eager chatter of the citizens as they wait, the cries of children at play, and the distant rush of mountain torrents. But then as a deep, hollow booming is heard from the dark recesses of the tunnel, an expectant hush falls upon the waiting throng. It is the sound of the giant bell of black metal, cast especially for this occasion, and hung around the neck of the leading animal.

Louder and louder grows the clanging, as the herd approaches, stiller and stiller the people until with all the drama of a star actor suddenly bursting upon the stage, the champion of champions emerges into the light and stands for a moment, framed by the dark mouth of the tunnel.

She presents a strange and beautiful sight. Around her soft, fawn-colored neck suspended from a shining dark leather collar hangs the huge copper bell decorated on all sides with silver hearts and stars and fitted with a silver clapper. This with her position as leader of the procession confirms her as best cow of the high pastures, best cow of the summer, best beast in the land.

On her forehead she wears a crimson heart or cross to in-

dicate her milk or cream has passed the average. But most
striking of all, revealing her as first in her herd in yield of milk,
butter, and cheese, her one-legged milking stool has been
affixed to the broad and noble head between the graceful
sweep of the horns.

It is tied there upside down like the gay hat of a maid in
spring, beribboned with streamers of the red and blue of
Liechtenstein, crimson and white, silver and gold. A wreath
fashioned of laurel leaves is woven about her head; cockades
of red, white, and blue are at her ears, bunches of meadow
flowers make gay the leather of her collar.

One can only gaze at her with astonishment and admiration,
for her simple, unobtrusive, natural beauty has been enhanced
a hundredfold.

The procession winds out of the long tunnel and down the
mountainside, the champions, the next best, the winners in
minor classes, each with heart or cross, or milking stool bound
upside down between her horns, then the horses garlanded and
bedecked, drawing the family carts, the herdsmen and dairymen wearing rosettes of colored ribbon on their shirts and
crimson and azure cockades in their hats, bearing signs "All
of us are returning." The signs too are cheered. No accidents,
no illnesses, no deaths. God has been good. Saint Rocchus and
Saint Ludmila, the holy Notburga, have watched over them
and kept them from harm. Another year has passed. In the
flower-garlanded carts the fat tubs of butter and the cheeses
piled high like red and yellow cannon balls denote prosperity
and the wealth that the Creator, through nature, has seen fit

to bestow upon his children.

And last of all, seemingly shamefaced, sad-eyed as though they knew that they had failed, without insignia, or touch of color at horns or flank, unattended except for the work dogs yapping at their heels and the herdsman's apprentice bringing up the rear, come those animals of more common breed or less energy, who have failed to distinguish themselves in the production of milk, or the percentage of butter fat in their cream, or good solid proteins in the cannon-ball cheeses. From their unhappy expressions you would almost swear they knew they were inferior.

By the time they emerge from the tunnel there is no one left to greet them, or even notice them; the crowds have gone off down the mountain, accompanying the colorful cavalcade of the successful beasts, leaving the others to bring up the rear as best they may.

It is a day of excitement, rejoicing, and felicitation, with the owners of the winners crowding the cafés and opening bottles of red Vaduzer wine to the herdsmen and dairymen. It is a great occasion for the winners.

No longer in the general rejoicing and carousing incident to this harvest ceremony is much thought directed toward the holy Notburga, that fourteenth-century milkmaid and simple serving girl who because of her piety, faith, and devotion to the Virgin Mary, became a saint under her given name of Ludmila, devoted to the care of Alpine cattle and their herdsmen.

The skiers returning in the winter at dusk from the slopes of

Malbun throw her hardly a glance, and the Ave that once used to be sung to her nightly by the herdsmen is now locked between the covers of a book instead of in the hearts of the people.

It was different in the old days, before belief in miracles, magic, and all the magical creatures that once inhabited the glens, ravines, and dark forests went from the mountains. Nature spoke more vividly to the people than it does today.

In those times there were still witches, elves, kobolds, and little hairy wild men, good and evil fairies and saints that took on human guise and came down from Heaven to assist the pious or punish the wicked. Werewolves roamed the slopes and the scaly dragon with poisonous breath and deadly sting inhabited the rocky caverns. Even the great eagles perched on lofty crags, peering down in search of the whistling marmots, were regarded with superstition.

It was just at the end of this period and the beginning of modern times, so say the old men who remember this bit as told by their mothers, or that version handed down in an old mountain song, along with some yellowed sheets of notes left by Father Polda in the tiny chapel at Steg, that the strange affair of the little weakling cow who was deemed good for nothing took place.

Perhaps it was not exactly as I am about to recount, for more than a century has gone by since these events happened, and the skull of the Weakling, as she was known, has weathered snow white at the feet of Saint Ludmila, where she stands benignly smiling in her niche. But the last time I visited her shrine I made my peace with her and asked in advance to be forgiven if I err. The expression carved on her countenance seemed to me tender and reassuring as though she knew that I too love these gentle and generous animals and have tried to do my best by one of them.

It was in the late summer of the year 1823; the herds were still pasturing in the Malbun and *Saminatals,* but the nights were already growing cool so that their days amidst the rich Alpine grass were numbered and the time of their annual descent into the *Rheintal* was not far off.

The setting sun had turned the blue sky a brilliant orange, then soft pink merging to pearl; the plum velvet of night had come out of the east, spangled with stars. The cattle were stamping and lowing softly in the stables nearby. The milking done, the herdsmen and dairymen gathered about the fire which the crisp air made welcome.

Father Polda had walked up from his little chapel in Steg, as was his nightly custom, to sit and talk with the men and

their families, for it was mostly under the sun and the stars
that he preached, or sought the God that he served.

Alois, the chief herdsman, wrapping his cloak around him,
arose and awakened the echoes with the mournful cry of the
ancient Ave he sent aloft each night:

"O-ho! O-ho! A-ve! Ave Maria!"

From the shadowed figures of the herders and dairymen
around the fire arose the words and simple melody of the
evensong of the herdsmen:

> *God, the Father, Creator of Heaven and earth,*
> *Give us your blessing, Watch o'er our hearth,*
> *Dearly beloved Mary and your dearly beloved Son,*
> *Let your protecting mantle spread o'er every one,*
> *St. Peter, Thou watchman at Heaven's gate,*
> *Shield us from savage beasts; in Thy hands our fate.*

The song swelled louder to include all the saints, Theodul,
Rocchus, Wendelin and Veit, Sebastian and St. Cyprian, each
of whom had particular duties to protect them from the mani-
fold dangers of the mountains, beasts of prey, witches, evil
spirits, avalanches of rock and snow, the claws of the bear,
the fangs of the wolf, the pounce of the lynx, the poisonous
breath and the stinging tail of the dragon.

And of course there was Ludmila, *die heilige Notburga,* to
whom they sang:

> *Sainted Ludmila, milkmaid without blame,*
> *Make flow rich milk in Holy Maria's name,*

Fill every udder; speak thy word,
To grace our beasts and bless our herd . . .

Father Polda smiled in the darkness. None of the saints had been left out. A big, generous man, he was meticulous with regard to the catalogue of the holy, and even though those whose duty it was to deal with witches and dragons might be thought to have been outmoded by the modernity that was coming to the mountains, he was glad they were still included for politeness' sake and memory of past favors, if nothing else.

Father Polda was a man of great and simple faith who believed in intercession, the force of prayer, and miracles, as opposed to chief herdsman Alois, who though professing belief, was hardheaded and as might be expected of one who lived out in the open and dealt with kine, practical and unsentimental.

Father Polda said: "It has been a good summer—the holy Notburga has done her work well—"

Alois grunted in the dark and lit his long curved pipe until the sparks flew. "There has been plenty of rain, which has made the pasturage rich and the yield good," he said. "It will be better than last year."

"Thanks be to God and Saint Ludmila who has interceded for us."

Alois grunted again. "Saint Ludmila has not been of much help to Johann Vospelt's weakling. Her yield is far below average. He was cheated when he bought that one."

"Ah," said Father Polda. "The little one with the white muzzle and the ribs showing. It is a pity. Johann needs the

money. He has not been well. He has a wife and small child. They spent all their savings to buy the cow."

"She is hardly worth taking to pasture," Alois declared. "She costs more than she can repay. Vospelt would be better off to butcher and sell her. She could not even feed her calf properly. I put it to Schädler's Luzerner champion, who has enough over for a dozen such. There is a beast for you. Butter fat 12 per cent, second yield of cream after the first is skimmed, and cheeses that weigh like stones." He puffed at his pipe a moment and added: "There is no animal in the herd that can touch her. She is practically certain to lead the procession for the second year for there is hardly more than a week left."

Father Polda did not reply at once, but sat hugging his knees under the black cassock, a huge lump of a man crouched by the fireside looking up into the starry sky behind which were all his friends, and reflecting. Finally he said in a voice that was singularly soft and gentle to emerge from such a giant:

"How unhappy the little Weakling must be. How miserable and wretched. I shall say a prayer for her."

Alois turned and stared at the priest over his pipe. "An animal has no feelings. Pray that Johann Vospelt gets rid of her before she costs him more than she has already."

But Father Polda was right, and Alois was wrong. The little Weakling was most miserable and unhappy indeed. For she was consumed by the hopeless desire to win the right to have her milking stool bedecked with gaily colored ribbons tied to her head at the summer's end.

It is doubtful whether she had dared dream of leading the

procession down from the mountainside, wearing the laurel wreath and the big, copper bell, for such was far beyond the capacities of a small, not too well-bred cow.

But that spring, when with the others of the mixed herd owned by the poorer peasants, she had made her slow, toilsome way up the mountain, through the tunnel and into the high pasturage, she was sure that at the very least she could earn a crimson heart or cross for her owner, and what her simple, gentle soul yearned for most dearly was the decoration of the milking stool to wear upon her head.

But the sad truth, as she and the herdsman soon learned, was that she was not very strong and her capacity limited. She was small and thin, and on the whole not to be compared with the huge, sturdy Alpine breeds from whom the milk fairly poured in great, warm, frothy, fragrant streams. Her health was not of the best and there were days when she gave no milk at all.

She was not particularly handsome, lacking the broad head, wide-set eyes, and long, curling eyelashes that gave the others the look of slightly aging beauty queens. She was taupe-colored, but darker and muddier in shade, thin-flanked and high-legged, and differed further from the others by her white muzzle, which made her look even paler and more delicate.

The Weakling tried very hard to be successful, but to little avail. As the weeks passed, she fell further and further behind in her yield. And the more she strained and fretted, the less she seemed to be able to produce.

She took her work seriously, eating heartily, cropping the

long, sweet grass indefatigably; she did not take too much exercise, or go climbing to higher pastures which might have disturbed her digestive processes; instead she lay quietly in the shade on hot afternoons, ruminating upon what it would be like to be crowned with the milking stool and cheered and acclaimed by the people. She chewed her cud carefully; she spent long hours thinking the proper thoughts about mother-hood and the responsibility of producing milk.

But no matter how hard she tried she could not seem to succeed. When the milker came around to her and pegged his one-legged stool into the clay floor of the stable, he would say: "Ach, it is hardly worth while to bring the pail to you, poor little Weakling." Nevertheless he would milk her out of kind-ness, for he was a good man, but the result would be no more than a third of a pail, or perhaps even less as the season wore on, with no froth or body to it, but instead a thin, bluish liquid that was deemed fit only to give to the pigs and chickens.

And the little Weakling would often turn her head and eye the slender, hand-turned milking stool, and so great was her yearning that she could almost feel what it would be like to have the seat touch her forehead between her small horns, and hear the rustle of the gaily colored ribbons as they bound it there. For hours afterward, as she stood in her stall, the spot on her brow between the horns would ache with longing for the contact.

The reason that the Weakling so greatly desired the reward of the milking stool was that she was feminine and through no fault of her own had been denied the physique and constitution that would enable her to play the part for which she had been put on earth. She yearned to give lavishly the sweet milk that humans craved for their children and for themselves, she wished to see herself the creator of tubs of creamy butter and round cannon balls of heavy yellow cheeses that would bring wealth to her owner. And female-like, she desired that adornment on the final day which turned the plainest of cows— which she had the misfortune to be—into the most ravishing creature. Capped with the milking stool, garlanded with paper flowers of all colors, beribboned in maroon and blue, she was sure she would please every eye and would arouse the admiration and appreciation of all.

You who believe that animals are dumb and incapable of reason or emotions similar to those experienced by humans will of course continue to do so. I ask you only to think of the yearning and heartache that is the lot of the poor and not-so-favored woman, as she stares through the glass of the shop window at a gay Easter hat, a particularly fetching frock, the sheerest of stockings, or a pair of shoes with little bows that seem to dance all by themselves; lovable articles, desirable articles, magic articles out of her reach since she can neither buy them, nor earn them as a gift, yet things that she knows would transform her in a moment from someone drab and unnoticed, into a sparkling queen, a ravishing beauty that would draw all eyes to her. Or, if not all eyes, then at least a few, and if not a few, then just one pair of eyes, and in the end, the only pair that mattered.

How deep and melancholy is the wish to be beautiful and

loved, to be lauded and admired, praised and desired. What power there lies behind the yearning within the feminine heart; what mountains have been moved, armies destroyed, thrones toppled, nations devastated, because of that feminine hunger for something bright, such as a ribbon, a bangle, a diamond, a crown, or the glitter in a man's eye. What civilizations have been built and worlds discovered to satisfy her craving for adornment, to confirm her belief that if only her body were outlined in silks from Cathay and her eyes ringed with kohl from Ind no man could resist her.

Can you really believe that such gigantic forces are engendered and shared only by humans, that this desire to be noticed and admired has not its counterpart in the animal kingdom?

If but the hundredth part of a woman's yearning from time to time for something beautiful to place upon her head, or at her throat, or in her ears, or on her back was what the little Weakling was experiencing in her desire to be distinguished as the most successful and desirable of her sex, then she was still the most miserable, unhappiest and most forlorn of all cows. For as the summer drew to a close she knew that her chances of succeeding were hopeless and that perhaps never in all her life would she taste that sweetness in the hour of triumph that was to come to her more fortunate companions.

It did not embitter her, however. It only made her sad, and increased the power of her yearning. She continued to see herself longingly, udders distended to aching with rich, creamy milk, and hear the welcome sound as it frothed into the pail until it filled to overflowing. And then she would feel the milk stool upon her head.

But by the end of the summer, the little Weakling was even more unprepossessing. She was gaunt, ungainly, her gait awkward, her udders slack and all but dry. Only her eyes preserved their luminosity and more than ever were filled with perpetual sadness.

One evening, when the herds had been grazing in the lower Samina Valley and were returning to Malbun for the night, Father Polda came forth from his little chapel and joined leathery old Alois, the chief herdsman, for his evening walk, and side by side they marched up the path alongside the mountain torrent, conversing to the peaceful rushing of the water that mingled with the musical jangling and tonkling of the deep-toned bells around the necks of the cattle.

They discussed the forthcoming descent, the bounty of the year, the prices that would be fetched in the market by the season's yield of butter and cheese, which would mean prosperity for all the valley, all except poor farmer Vospelt whose weakling cow had yielded so little.

Thus the subject of the Weakling was revived, and Father Polda noted that they had already passed the shrine of Saint Ludmila in her niche in the rock. He had meant in passing to say another prayer for the little cow, to ask the holy Notburga to intercede not only for the unfortunate animal, but also for farmer Vospelt, who needed the money so much for his family. He realized that it was too late for such intercession to do much good unless by a miracle, but he also believed there was no harm in trying.

They heard a sharp barking, and as they looked back they saw that Alois' work dog was yapping at the heels of the poor Weakling, who as usual had fallen behind the others in the ascent, and was making no attempt to continue, nor was she paying the slightest attention to the animal baying at her heels.

Instead, as the two men gazed they could see that she had turned broadside to the path and was standing staring across the white-frothed torrent to the figure of Saint Ludmila, or rather the doll-like image of her that had been created by Anton the woodcarver of Steg, many, many years ago.

Since there were no pictures extant of *die heilige Notburga*, the woodcarver had taken the expression he had carved on her face from his own heart, one that had likewise loved the gentle members of the Creator's animal kingdom to whom He had assigned the task of extending the bounty of their mother-hood to man.

Thus her smile was warm, tender, loving and yet infinitely pitying too, and invited a similar expression to the lips of all those who passed and paused, and many, seeing her, would murmur: "Dear Saint Ludmila, holy Notburga, give the sweetness and warmth of your protection to me likewise."

And so the two men saw Saint Ludmila smiling down at the little Weakling, and the Weakling standing there, unmindful of the dog that other times would have terrified her, and gazing up at the holy Notburga, her eyes filled with hopeless and gentle pleading as well as the infinite longing and love that filled her being.

Alois said to Father Polda: "Your little Weakling has grown impatient, waiting for your prayers." He laughed good-humoredly. "It looks as though she has decided to ask Saint Ludmila to intercede for her herself. She's gone one ahead of you, Father."

But Father Polda was not amused, for the saints and prayer were something he took seriously, and he rebuked Alois angrily for levity verging on blasphemy.

"The Heavenly Father takes all animals both great and small under His shelter," he said, "but He did not give them the capacity to pray. That is for us to do for them, else He would have bestowed upon them the power of speech. You should not joke about such matters."

Alois, who for all of his hardheadedness was a believer and who also was a little afraid of Father Polda, mumbled in his

square brown beard that he had not meant to give offense, whistled to his dog, and they turned up the mountain path again and soon the little Weakling came trotting after.

But this time it was perhaps Father Polda who was wrong, and the herdsman who could have been right.

For a prayer need not be a rhetorical address, or an itemized petition, or lips moved soundlessly inside a cathedral, or even words spoken into the air. A prayer may be a wordless inner longing, a sudden outpouring of love, a yearning within the soul to be for a moment united with the infinite and the good, a humbleness that needs no abasement or speech to express it, a cry in the darkness for help when all seems lost, a song, a poem, a kind deed, a reaching for beauty, or the strong, quiet inner reaffirmation of faith.

A prayer in fact can be anything that is created of God that turns to God.

The little Weakling did not know that she was praying when she paused on the path, her eyes caught by the bright object shining from the niche in the rock. She was aware of nothing but the sadness in her being and unutterable longing to pour forth her love in the shape of milk and thereafter to satisfy her yearning for the beribboned milking stool to be given her.

There is no way she could express or articulate this hunger, but it was particularly strong that evening as she returned with her udders almost flat. The figure in the rocks caught her gentle eyes. She turned to it in the moment when it seemed as though her unhappiness and shame would overwhelm her, and she stood there trembling with the intensity of her desire to be as all the others and know the joy of giving as well as receiving.

And so, in a sense she made a prayer, and having done so, it existed; it was loosed. It was directed at the figure of the one whose love and duty called for her to intercede at the throne; and as with all prayers that arise from the sincere and loving heart, it was both heard and felt, in the far corners of the universe. For whereas evil has no power to extend beyond its own radius, the loving trust of a child, or the whispered confession of a sincere and tender heart can alter the stars in their courses. The gentle plea of a maid, asking for a bit of ribbon or cambric for her hair rings as loudly as the Cardinal's Latin in the outer spaces of time or thought, whence destiny is directed.

Surely you do not think that God is angry at the desires of his creatures to win affection and appear beautiful and desirable in the eyes of others. For He Himself loves beauty since He created so much of it on the face of the earth in both man and beast. And who but He caused the peasants of Liechtenstein to think of something so gay, innocent, and charming as the wreathing of their beasts with laurel and garlands when the year's harvest was garnered, and crowning them with the insignia of their gentle serviture, the milking stool?

It was the next day that Alois decided to take the cattle for the last time up to the highest pasture just below the *Sareiserjoch* where the green slopes are watered by crystal springs that gush from the rocks.

As the herdsmen and dogs marshaled the beasts for the

climb, for the pasture lay a thousand feet above them, his eyes fell upon the Weakling, and he found himself torn between a mixture of annoyance as he remembered the reproof of Father Polda administered the night before, and pity for the animal that was so thin and generally ill-favored. He genuinely loved the animals that had been entrusted to his care, and watched over them.

As he looked, he thought of the long climb and the poor condition of the beast, as well as the plight of farmer Vospelt should the animal die on the heights and have to be sold for what her hide would bring for leather. And, too, there was the celebration and descent to be thought of, now less than a week away. It would be foolish to take chances, for it was a part of the custom that if during the season there was an accident, or one of the animals died, the ceremony of the milking stools, the ribbons, and the gay decorations was dispensed with for that year.

He said to the herdsmen: "Let her be, the little Weakling. She is not worth taking to the high pasture now. She is out of the running for the prizes, anyway. Let her remain down here where she will be safe."

And then he called to his youngest daughter, aged seven, who was playing nearby, and who too was named Ludmila after *die heilige Notburga:* "Ludmila, come here. Look after the little Weakling today and see that she comes to no harm. She is to remain behind. Do not let her stray out of your sight and see that she is back in the stall by sundown."

And with that the dogs were set to work, the herdsmen cried

"Heuh!" Beasts and herders set off up the mountain.

Little Ludmila had brown legs and arms, a brown face, and brown hair, but her eyes were as blue as the cornflowers and wild delphinium that grew in the mountain meadows. She went at once and put her arms around the little Weakling's neck and laid her cheek next its soft, white muzzle, and then taking hold of the end of her halter marched off with her, with the Weakling following on docilely behind, her bell giving off a musical clang with every other step she took.

Some children would have been upset at having their day's play disturbed by such a peremptory order to take charge of a derelict animal that was not good for much of anything, but Ludmila was pleased, for she had for a long time wished to go into the dark glen at the foot of the *Bettlerjoch* a short distance away to look for elves which she was sure lived there.

She was afraid to go alone, for there might be other things there as well, such as witches, or little hairy wild men with peaked hats and long noses and ears who hid behind rocks with only the tips of their ears and the points of their hats showing, or even perhaps a small dragon.

But with the little cow along as her companion, her bronze bell tonkling loudly to frighten away any evil spirits, and her warm and comforting presence there and the halter to cling to, Ludmila felt no fear at all, and soon child and beast were lost to sight as they left the little community at Malbun and chose the path toward Gritsch and the deep wild glen at the bottom of the *Bettlerjoch.*

The sturdy brown legs took the child over a winding Alpine

road that soon plunged into a dark pine forest. Shortly they came to a spot where the path split in two and on the right descended sharply into a dark and rocky ravine where fallen trees were tumbled like jackstraws and the boulders lay strewn about as though flung by a giant hand.

This was the mysterious ravine of the *Bettlerjoch*. Mounting, it grew wilder and more tumultuous until it reached to that mass of granite pillars and monoliths with the curiously human forms which legend said were the Butter Beggars, those wandering friars who came over the pass known as the *Nenzinger Himmel* through the *Joch* to the high pasturage to beg for butter for the cold winter days to come and in return bestowed their blessings on herdsmen and herds and prayed for them, and who one day were overtaken by a terrible storm and their forms frozen there forever.

But descending, the terrain grew less wild; there were little patches of grass and meadow with many herbs and wildflowers that seemed to flourish nowhere else.

For a moment, Ludmila hesitated to enter this unfamiliar territory, but the Weakling's bell jangled reassuringly, and when the animal also gave forth a soft "Moo," she hesitated no longer, and taking the halter once more in her chubby fist entered the side of the ravine by the right-hand path and descended to the glen below.

The elves were there in the form of splinters of sunlight flashing from the quartz in the granite, or filtering through the greenery, dappling the leaves of the trees, and the child pursued them deeper and deeper into the ravine until they vanished in the darkness of tumbled rock or cave, or dense pines where the sun no longer penetrated.

Soon they came to a kind of glade opening out from the lower part of the glen through a rocky path. Here the land

leveled for a space, a rushing brook quietened, as it meandered
through this hidden meadow ringed with trees, and rich with
sweet-smelling herbs and flowers, yellow blossoms with broad
leaves amongst ferns, lichens, and algae, arenarias and saxi-

frages growing amidst dark grasses.

The little Weakling commenced to feed contentedly, shaded by a gigantic oak tree that spread its branches in huge circumference and beneath which, amidst a scattering of sweet acorns, the flowering herbs and weeds grew in thick profusion.

Comforted by the sound of the bell about the neck of the Weakling and her eager munching, Ludmila explored the boundaries of what was obviously a magic circle on enchanted ground; watching the long blue shadows of the trout as they sunned themselves in the brook, discovering a gray badger with shining eyes working at the mouth of his hole, startling a young deer, coming upon a whole family of little hamsters feeding on acorns and noting hundreds of tiny green-breasted finches and blue-headed tits flitting through the branches of the trees and peering out from behind the leaves.

And in this manner, with the Weakling feeding placidly, and the child, herself turned into the very kind of woodland and mountain elf she sought, playing in and about the beautiful glen and all its wild things, time passed. The shadows grew longer, the air cooler, and the sun began to dip toward the jagged rim of the mountain peaks visible through the trunks of the tall pines, and her instincts told Ludmila that it was time to return home.

But the day had been long, exciting, and strenuous, and she was both hungry and thirsty. And since she was a herdsman's daughter, Ludmila knew both where and how to provide herself with food and went directly to the source.

She secured the Weakling's trailing halter and led her to a sapling where she made her fast. Then seating herself at the hind quarters she took one of the soft teats, directed it at her mouth, closed her eyes, and began to milk.

At the touch of the little hands, so different from the rough, strong, horny palms of the herdsmen, it seemed as though a shudder ran through the Weakling. For the first moment as the child tugged, first at one then at another, there was no response. Not even the thin bluish trickle rewarded her efforts. But again, the shudder shook the animal and she stood there, her feet spread apart, trembling as though in the grip of a mountain chill. All her pent-up anguish seemed to find expression in the single cry, half a moo and half a moan that came from her throat and echoed from the pillars that represented the frozen friars of the *Bettlerjoch* above and went sighing off into the peaks. And then her milk began to flow.

A few drops at first, then a trickle, then a stream, and soon, a warm, rich, fragrant jet shot into the mouth of Ludmila, causing her to gurgle and laugh with surprise, pleasure, and satisfaction, a sound which surely to the Weakling must have been the most beautiful she had ever heard. At last, she was giving, as God had intended her to do.

The child drank until she could hold no more, and thereafter led the Weakling to the stream to let her refresh herself, and then taking her in tow, set off through the rocky path that led from the enchanted meadow, through the glen and up the ravine on the homeward path. And for the first time since she had matured, the Weakling, her heart filled with joy, felt the ache of plenitude in her udders and the need to be further relieved of the gift she carried there.

That night, when the herdsmen, accompanying their proud, sleek cattle, returned from the high pasturage by the *Sareiserjoch*, to the huts and stables just below the slopes of Malbun and the milkers took to their metal pails and one-legged milking stools, the miracle of Saint Ludmila, the holy milkmaid Notburga, began.

The Weakling was already standing in her stall, emitting low moos, of pleasurable pain, when from force of habit the milker arrived at her side, set stool and pail, seized the nearest teat and squeezed perfunctorily, for he was weary from serving the heavy yielders and was grateful that the day was drawing to a close.

But the first sound of the powerful stream of milk landing with a clang at the bottom of the pail awoke him and caused him to cry out in amazement, as by the light of the lantern that hung from the roof of the milking shed he saw the distended skin of the swollen udders bearing such a burden as he had never encountered before in this unfortunate little animal.

He remembered the poor quality of her yield and still by habit, milked on, but when the pail was half full, his cry arose over the stamping of the hoofs in the shed, the switching of tails, and the rush of the milk—"Hola, Alois! Hola there, send for Alois. The chief herdsman is to come here at once to see what has happened."

Alois came and stared likewise, for now the pail was three-quarters filled with creamy liquid topped by foaming bubbles of fatty froth, as rich as any that ever came from the big Swiss champions in the herd.

The pail was filled to overflowing, another was placed beside her, once again the powerful jet of milk clanged against the empty sides, the liquid, warm and pungent, began to foam as it climbed up the pail. The other milkers and herders crowded into the shed as word spread of the astonishing thing that was happening to the little Weakling, and a moment later there was a movement in the throng and the huge bulk of Father Polda bent over to pass through the door.

He glanced at the full milk pail, the second filling beneath the fingers of the milker, the color of the fluid and the oily quality of the froth that topped it, and crossed himself.

"Holy Saint Ludmila, Holy Notburga!" he cried. "It is a miracle!" for he wished it so.

Alois grunted as was his custom when he was about to become hardheaded and did not wish to admit something, especially to the priest. "Some of these sickly ones come into milk late sometimes. We will see. The milk may be sour, or deficient. Wait until it has been separated."

At last the udders were emptied, the second pail was nearly filled and taken away to be tested for fat and butter content, darkness fell, supper was eaten and the men gathered about the fire, and once again the Mountain Ave rang out—"O-ho! O-ho! A-ve! Ave Maria!"—when the herdsman whose duty it was to watch by night by the stables came running into the circle, pale and out of breath:

"Alois! Father Polda! The one with the white muzzle, the

little Weakling that was milked last tonight! I heard her complaining and went with the lantern to look. Her udders are filled again. She must be milked at once. Come and see if you do not believe me."

It was true. Scarce three hours had passed, but the milk sacs were again distended and heavy with their burden. A milker was hastily summoned, and again the rich, yellowish liquid thundered into the pail; once more a second receptacle had to be fetched to hold the yield.

Father Polda crossed himself again and cried: "Holy Saint Ludmila, a miracle, a miracle indeed. Well, Alois, what have you to say now?"

But the chief herdsman did not reply. He only stared bewildered at this amazing thing, though it was noted that he crossed himself likewise.

In the meantime, a layer of heavy, yellowish cream, six inches deep, and so thick that one might have stood up a spoon in it without its falling over had gathered at the top of the first two pails that the little Weakling had filled earlier. Here was butter fat and a wealth of it such as had not been seen produced on the high pasturage within living memory.

All through the night and the next day and the next after that it went on. Replenishing herself, it seemed, with no more than copious draughts from buckets of water, the Weakling continued to give of her so long withheld riches every three or four hours, wearing out relays of milkmen whose arms became heavy and fingers cramped as they worked to relieve her of her sudden treasure.

Word began to travel of the miracle that was taking place and mountaineers and woodcutters, keepers of hospices and charcoal burners from the neighboring peaks and valleys came over to the milking shed in Malbun to see for themselves, and soon there was no room inside for everyone and so the gentle little creature with the white muzzle, thin flanks, and tender eyes was moved out into the open where all could see her and watch the fabulous torrents of milk that poured from her.

She stood there then in a kind of daze, wrapped in the glory of bestowing and the fulfillment of that part of her yearning that had to do with udders filled with life-giving food and drink that now was hers to share.

On the third day, the head dairyman came bustling from the cheese and butter factories next the milking shed in a state of excitement, shouting: "One more pail, and the little one will win best of her group. She already has heart and cross won and needs only another gallon to catch up and surpass the best of her herd. It does not seem possible."

It was Father Polda who replied: "Oh, yes. With a miracle, everything is possible, when there is faith in goodness and belief in the Creator whose will has called forth greater things even than this. She may even, who knows, be the first cow through the tunnel at Steg, bearing the bell and garland of victory—"

But here Alois and his hard head were heard from. "That cannot be," he said. "Schädler's Luzerner has won the right of first cow by many tens of pounds. It will be impossible for the little one to overtake her. For the woodcutter who has just arrived over the *Bettlerjoch* tells me that the first snow has appeared on the *Panülerkopf* and the *Hornspitz.* Tomorrow we return to the valley."

Father Polda sighed and said nothing, for the word of the chief herdsman in all things pertaining to the herds entrusted to his care was law, and no one dared question his commands. But it being Father Polda's first personal miracle, he wished to see it taken to a climax.

At that, the Weakling barely made the final pail that was needed to give her the honor of the milking stool. For the great and miraculous flow seemed at last to come to an end, and it was all that the milkers could do to wring the last drops from her fabulous udders. Yet achieve it she did though the effort left her weak and spent and she was led on tottery legs to the shelter of the stall, fed and watered and allowed to rest for the great event of the descent the following day.

And thus it was that the poor little Weakling, whose hopes of realizing her desire to be decorated with her milking stool had seemed so utterly impossible of fulfillment, was led forth the next day, cleaned, washed, brushed, so that thin and emaciated as she was, her dun-colored hide glistened. Hoofs and horns were polished until they sparkled in the sunlight and at last came the moment when she felt the seat of the milking stool pressed against her head between the horns by rough but kind hands and lashed there with gaily-colored ribbons.

Streamers were fastened to the stool's leg, paper flowers

and cockades attached to her headstall and about her ears; garlands of flowers hung about her neck. Small-boned, and lacking the stalwart maturity of the older animals, her head graced by the decorations, her sweetness of expression gave her the air of a young girl going to her first ball. She became suddenly innocently beautiful and heart-warmingly radiant.

Now, word of the event that had taken place on the high pasturage had also reached to the village of Vaduz, which heard the rumor of how the poor peasant Vospelt's animal that had been last in yield of dairy products had in the final three days, by the intervention of Saint Ludmila, poured forth a miraculous stream of milk.

Outside the tunnel, the crowds gathered to wait in twice the number they ever had before. They came up from Vaduz, the capital, and Schaan and Triesen, Mäls and Balzers, Nendeln and Eschen, to climb the lofty Triesenberg on foot and take up their position of vantage at Gnalp, to see for themselves whether there was any truth in the strange marvel that had been reported from the fastnesses of the high pasturage.

Because it might be an ecclesiastical affair, if true, the Herr Canonicus Josef from the big church in Vaduz was there with lesser members of the clergy from the vicinity, and since if it were actually so it would redound to the eternal credit of Liechtenstein, a member of the ruling family from the *Schloss* below arrived, incognito of course.

Spontaneously, and without invitation, the brass band from Schaanwald appeared, the *Männerchor* from Planken and the girl singers from Mauren and Ruggell. The *Bürgermeister* of Vaduz came in his robes as did the president of the council and the ministers from Switzerland and Austria.

Naturally the attraction was likewise to see which would be the lead cow this year, but behind the huge turnout lay excitement of perhaps witnessing a marvel of some sort. It could of course hardly be true that the poor, sickly little animal they all remembered as belonging to peasant Vospelt, and which few had deemed worth even sending up to the high pasturage, could really have won a prize, much less the decoration of the milking stool, but if there was any truth in the rumors, they were all there and prepared to see.

In Malbun the cavalcade was ready for the descent. Cattle, horses, men, women, children, dogs, all were groomed and dressed in their best and decorated in every manner possible to mark the wonderful occasion.

An hour after sunup the procession gathered on the meadow nearby the little community of huts, sheds, and barns where they had all lived together during the long summer and the doors and windows of which were now boarded up.

Father Polda stood upon a drinking trough and blessed them, as was his custom, and sent up a prayer of gratitude to Saint Ludmila for the miracle she had created for them. Then with cries from the herders, the cracking of whips, the barking of dogs, and the gay singing of the women and children, they started down the Malbun, next the roaring torrent to Steg.

First in the line, the silver clapper of the great brazen bell about her neck booming her approach, came Schädler's great champion Luzerner, winning beast the second year in succession, milk stool worn proudly as one who was used to such articles borne upon her head. Then came Gruber's Frisian, and Wohlmayr's Züricher champion in second and third place, followed by several others that had ranked high. Thereafter proudly heading the last division of the mixed herd belonging to many poor peasants tottered the little Weakling with her gay decorations and sweet exalted expression, looking like a mixture of half cocotte, half angel. At her head marched Ludmila, cornflowers the color of her eyes braided in her brown hair. At her side walked Father Polda.

The three came eventually to the shrine of the holy Notburga by the torrent Malbun, and here they paused and turned to her as though by mutual understanding and consent, the huge man in the black cassock, the brown, barelegged child, and the Weakling. No word was spoken. Ludmila had her arm about the neck of the animal, and together they stood by the wooden rail that guarded people from falling into the stream and looked across the silvery waters to the figure in the niche, the sweet little doll with the tender expression on her carved and painted countenance.

On the child's face was wonder. In the eyes of the Weakling was deathless love. On the lips of Father Polda was a prayer. There they remained thus for a long time, so long that chief herdsman Alois returned to see what was holding up the procession and thus he found them.

When her father came up, the child suddenly left the little cow and ran to him, put her arms around his neck and began to cry, causing him to say: "Now now, Ludmila, what is the matter? Why are you crying?"

"Because of my little cow who is so beautiful. Saint Ludmila wishes her to lead all the others."

The chief herdsman was much less hardheaded when it came to his daughter and he smiled at her and said: "She does,

does she? And how would you know this?"

Ludmila stopped crying and took her father's hand and led him to the rail, looked across to Saint Ludmila and replied: "Because she spoke to me, and *told me so*. Please, papa, let her be the first."

Alois looked from his daughter to the Weakling, to Father Polda standing at her side and said harshly: "What is this nonsense? Have you been putting ideas into the child's head? What does she mean the saint spoke to her? Did you hear anything?"

Father Polda smiled, and gently shook his head. "I heard nothing," he said. "But sometimes little children can hear things that we cannot."

For a moment the big, bearded herdsman stood there staring at the statue. Then he picked up the child on his arm and strode away down the path. Man and beast followed.

But at Steg, the last stopping place before they moved down the *Saminatal* and entered the rock tunnel to emerge into the world beyond, chief herdsman Alois gave brief and sharp orders; two herdsmen came to the rear of the procession and led the little Weakling forward to the head of the line. There, while many looked aghast and all stared in utter amazement, they took the great black-silver star and heart-studded bell with the polished black leather collar from the leading cow and hung it about her neck. They likewise removed the crown of laurel leaves from the noble brow of the Luzerner champion and draped it about the head of the Weakling, for whom it was too big, and therefore fell slightly askew, giving her an even more coquettish air. In her emaciated state from the great effort she had made, the weight of the big bell was almost more than she could carry. Then the halter lead was put into the hands of Ludmila. The Weakling staggered forward and the two, now at the head of the procession, led the way down the road into the tunnel.

It was wrong and arbitrary, what Alois did, for Schädler's big Luzerner had fairly won the right to lead them all home a second year and one voice from the crowd protested, "Halloo there, Mr. Chief Herdsman, what is going on? Everyone knows that Schädler's animal is the winner."

But with a terrible frown, Alois cried, "Quiet! Saint Ludmila herself has commanded that the Weakling lead us home!" And thereafter none dared dispute his decision.

Soon the dense crowds lining both sides of the road on the other side of the tunnel heard the irregular booming of the big cowbell around the neck of the approaching leader. It would ring, then stop, then ring faintly, again louder as it approached, more faintly again, and once it jangled harshly as though the bearer had fallen.

Murmurs and shivers of excitement ran through the crowd. Louder and louder sounded the great bell and steadier now. The moment was at hand.

Out of the mouth of the tunnel stepped a brown elf with cornflowers the color of her eyes braided through her brown hair, leading a small thin cow with a white muzzle, belled, crowned, and garlanded. For a moment they stood blinking in the sunlight. Then a great shout went up from the throng,

almost like a hosanna, a cheer and a cry and a greeting and a prayer all in one. Men waved their hats and shouted, women wept and sobbed.

It was true. The miracle had taken place, for there was the evidence before their very eyes. Not only had the poor despised Weakling won the right to wear her milk stool, but the champion's laurels and winner's position, the prize of best cow of the year had come to her. Only a saint could have made this possible.

Then the brass band struck up the national anthem of Liechtenstein, the *Männerchor* burst into song as did the

Sängerbund of girls from Mauren and Ruggell, and the women's choir from Triesenberg.

His Highness, the member of the Royal family, dropped his incognito and stepped forward to pin a glittering medal, the Royal Double Eagle First Class to the Weakling's collar and pick up the child Ludmila in his arms and kiss her. Herr Canonicus Josef suddenly knelt in the road, followed by the other members of the clergy, and struck up an "Alleluia" and the next moment men, women, and children in the huge throng of welcomers likewise went to their knees, singing and giving thanks to Him and those on High from Whom all miracles and blessings flow.

And so, her greatest desire and dream of glory came to realization, the little Weakling, burdened with the earthly prizes awarded to her by Heavenly dispensation, looked out upon this strange scene, the towering mountains opposite, the blue thread of the Rhine in the valley far below, the people in their Sunday best kneeling in the road, the black-robed priests, the stately figure of His Highness, and her eyes were gentle and swimming, filled with love and happiness, that all this which she had so much desired had in the end happened to her, and that before her final moment she had been privileged to give.

For the effort and the strain of the last three days had been too much for her, and with that sure instinct of animals, she knew she was looking upon the sunshine and the kindly people whom it had been her duty to feed for the last time. And she was content.

The big bell boomed again. The sun glittered from the golden medal at her collar. Child and animal started forward again down the mountain followed by the gay and colorful procession of the annual return from the high pasturage.

There is not much more to the story. Worn out by her efforts, the little Weakling passed away in the valley before sundown that evening. Yet strangely it did not put a damper on the celebration, or the happiness of the people at having been singled out for the execution of a miracle in their midst. They and the Canonicus saw it quite simply as the logical extension of the miracle whereby, having performed it and demonstrated her love and power via the Weakling, Saint Ludmila, the holy Notburga had taken the little animal to her as her reward and she would henceforth graze peacefully and happily in the Heavenly pastures close to the side of her loving friend and patron. And it is for this reason that the skull and horns of the Weakling were bestowed on the shrine of the saint.

The butter and cheese made from the miraculous milk of the Weakling brought their weight in gold and never again would the poor peasant Vospelt or his family want for anything.

Only one thing more remains to be told.

A week later, chief herdsman Alois suddenly appeared at

Steg in the Samina Valley with the child Ludmila at his side and sought out Father Polda in the tiny chapel.

"Come," he said to the priest. "Come with us."

They walked, all three in silence up the path again past the shrine in the rocks to which Alois did not so much as vouchsafe a glance now, until they came to the deserted huts and barns on the Malbun slope. Here it was that the little Ludmila at her father's behest took over the leadership, and with the sure orientation of the mountain child, led them up the path to the *Bettlerjoch.* As she had once before, she branched off from the main dark and fearsome ravine downward toward the glen of the elves, and thence through the rock path to the magic circle in the enchanted meadow peaceful in the morning sun with only the sound of birds in the great oak, the rustling of small animals in the underbrush, and the gentle murmur of the stream resting before it resumed its plunge below.

Alois now roved about this meadow, his eyes on the ground; he went to the brook, came back, knelt near the oak tree and examined the ground, arose and went to the opposite side and did the same. And as he searched, his dark, bearded face lit up with satisfaction and at last he came over and faced Father Polda.

"Well," asked the priest. "Why have you brought me here? What is it you have discovered?"

"This," said Alois. "Look there. Do you recognize that little weed with the yellow flower and the broad leaf?"

Father Polda gazed down at the plant that seemed to be

growing in unusual profusion all about them. "It is the *Alchemilla*," he replied. "The *Mutterkraut*."

"Yes," said the herdsman. "Have you ever seen so much at one time?"

The priest shook his head. "No. It is most unusual."

"Ah! Then come here and look. Here under the oak tree, it grows almost solid. But see where it has been cropped, and the hoof marks of an animal. Round and about this tree it has been eaten away—"

"Well—?" said the priest.

Alois threw him a look of triumph. "It was here that Ludmila came that day with the little Weakling when I refused to take her along to the high pasture. Those are her hoofmarks. The little one in a few hours found and consumed more *Mutterkraut* than most Alpine cattle would in a lifetime. The whole day she grazed upon the *Alchemilla*. In the evening, her milk glands violently stimulated, she started to give milk." He smiled in triumph again and looked the priest in the eye. "There is your miracle of Saint Ludmila for you. It is explained as I always knew it must be."

The priest remained silent and his eyes were bent to the ground where the hoofprints of the little Weakling were still plain to be seen as well as the close-to-the-ground cropped ends of many of the *Alchemilla* plants which somehow had flourished in this secluded place.

"Well," asked the chief herdsman, "what have you to say?"

The priest looked up, but his brow was unclouded and his

eyes untroubled and clear. "Yes," he said finally. "You are right. The miracle is indeed explained for all of those for whom the miracles must always be explained lest humans be forced to confess that they are not as important as they believe themselves to be."

Alois said: "You admit then that now we know why all of a sudden the Weakling gave so much milk and of such high content that in the end it was like giving her heart's blood and strength and it killed her?"

A little smile now played about the lips of the big priest. "That is correct," he said. "Now we know why the little one suddenly gave so much milk. Ah, yes, now we know everything."

"Eh?" said Alois, suspiciously, struck by something in the tone of the priest. "What do you mean by everything?"

"Oh," replied Father Polda, still smiling, "all the other miracles which you will explain to me—what made you say that day the little Weakling was praying at the shrine of Saint Ludmila, what was it that led you to decide against taking the animal to the high pasturage that day, how you came to entrust her to little Ludmila's care—also of course how the child came to wander here to this deserted glen where no ordinary child would venture alone, and how together they discovered this marvelous patch of *Mutterkraut*—and finally of course the greatest wonder of all, what made you decide in one moment to listen to your child, go against the records and at the last minute name the Weakling champion cow and leader of the descent into the valley, thus setting the final stamp and seal on the miracle in which you do not believe."

He paused and offered his hand to the child who took it confidingly. "Come," he said, "let us go from here." He turned to Alois still smiling gently, "But there will be time for those explanations later—"

He walked slowly hand in hand with Ludmila back the way they had come through the rocky defile. Behind them Alois walked silently, his head bent toward the ground as one in deep thought. . . .